GOOD DOG,
BAD DOG

This is for Mum and Dad, with love.

With thanks to Joel Stewart, Emma Bonsall,
Portia Rosenberg, Woodrow Phoenix and Pam Smy.

Enormous extra special thanks to Faz and
to Lovely Ben Sharpe.

More brilliant books from the DFC Library:

THE SPIDER MOON
by Kate Brown

MEZOLITH
by Ben Haggarty & Adam Brockbank

GOOD DOG, BAD DOG

A DAVID FICKLING BOOK 978 0 385 61825 0

First published thanks to the amazing DFC weekly comic,
May 2008 – March 2009 (Come back soon!!)

This edition published in Great Britain in 2010 by David Fickling Books,
a division of Random House Children's Books
A Random House Group Company

1 3 5 7 9 10 8 6 4 2

Copyright © Dave Shelton, 2010

DAVID FICKLING BOOKS
31 Beaumont Street, Oxford, OX1 2NP

www.**kidsatrandomhouse**.co.uk
www.**rbooks**.co.uk

Addresses for companies within The Random House Group Limited can be found at:
www.randomhouse.co.uk/offices.htm

THE RANDOM HOUSE GROUP Limited Reg. No. 954009

A CIP catalogue record for this book is available from the British Library.

Printed and bound in China

GOOD DOG, BAD DOG

Written & drawn by Dave Shelton

Golden Bone coloured by Faz Choudhury

David Fickling Books

OXFORD · NEW YORK

DOG MEETS DOG

5

Meanwhile, down on the ground...

Excuse me, officer...

I'm Detective McBoo. I was meant to meet Detective Bergman at HQ, but I missed him. Is he here?

Oh, hello, Sir. Yes, Detective Bergman is in pursuit of a suspect in the McCay Building over there.

Oh yes? Do you think he'll be long?

Um, difficult to say, Sir. You'd better see for yourself.

Oh deary me!

Crikey! I'd better go and help out. You stay here. And radio for an ambulance.

Just in case.

JAMES W McKIE BUILDING 1932

James "Wheels" Dupree, I am arresting you on suspicion of a whole bunch of bad stuff...

You have the right to remain silent. And I suggest you do. I'm in no mood to chat.

Whatever you say, Bergman, just don't let go of my leg!

LIFT OUT OF ORDER

Oh dear!

SMASH!

Eh?

Oh!

Uh?

OOF!

OOP!

OOH!

CRASH!

Wow!

Ow!

Ooooh!

Detective Bergman, let me introduce myself. I'm your new partner, Duncan McBoo.

Sorry I'm late.

That's okay. Good of you to drop by!

Excuse us, folks. Sorry about the mess.

Okay, McBoo, let's get Dupree here back to HQ.

The sooner we get him to tell us who he was robbing banks with last week, the sooner we get to go and do something really dangerous!

I tell ya, Bergman, I was the other side of town visiting my granny.

Quit wasting my time, Dupree! I've got better things to do than listen to your fairy stories!

We know you drove the car for the Bagel Street robbery. Now tell me who the stick-up guy was and I'll go easy on you.

Ah, can it, Bergman! You've got nothing on me and we both know it. Stop being such a dummy, let me go and you can go chase some pigeons or somethin'.

Don't you **ever** call me a dummy, Wheels Dupree!

Erk!

I'll tear your tail off and shove it up—

Eek!

Tea and cake, Mr Dupree?

Oh, so it's the old good cop/bad cop routine, is it? Can't you chumps be a bit more original?

I don't know what you mean. Now be careful, this tea is very ...

... hot! Oop!

OW! OW!
OW!

Oh, I'm so sorry, Mr Dupree...

WAH!

slip

OOF!

SQUISH!

OW!

Ooooooh! Okay, okay...

I did the bank job with Gruff Growler, okay? He's holed up in Apartment 13, Longden House.

Now get off me, will ya?

Let's go, partner.

Nice work, McBoo.

9

Longden House

94,000, 95,000, 96,000... Ho boy!

Who's that?

KNOCK KNOCK

POLICE!

Open up, Growler!

Erk!

Luckily, I can make a quick exit down the old fire escape.

EEK!

Hello, Mr Growler, lovely day. Off out for a stroll?

Now, I'm afraid I am going to have to arrest you. I do hope that's okay?

Uh, yeah, sure thing, copper.

Oh good. I do so hate any ...

... unpleasantness.

Oh dear.

Stick 'em up, copper!

Oh well, now this is just rude!

Here, Shorty – make yourself useful and carry this.

Oof!

Now, let's go down to my car. And no funny business or I plug the big fella!

Heh! This is funny. My own police escort helping me to get away!

Hmf!

Funny?

I'd wipe the smile off your ugly face soon enough if you weren't hiding behind that gun!

Maybe so.

But I **have** got this gun...

And my face ain't as ugly as I'm about to make yours!

Oh, Growler...

Big mistake pointing the gun at me!

You're the one who's...

Uh?

SLAP!

Now then, Mr Growler, as I was saying...

BLAM

Eek!

THE GOLDEN BONE OF ALEXANDRIA

A burglary? It's an outrage!

Twenty-one years on the force ... murders, kidnappings, bank heists ...

... and they waste my time with a burglary case? It's embarrassing!

Aye, well, it's no ordinary burglary.

The thieves got away with...

... THE GOLDEN BONE OF ALEXANDRIA!

Sir Garfield Woofington, I presume?

Yes, yes, quite.

So you're the young pups who are going to track down the brigands who've robbed me, eh?

Cardigan, get these fellows some drinks would you?

Certainly, Sir.

Gentlemen?

Bourbon.

No ice.

Banana milk-shake please.

No ice for me either.

The bounders seem to have broken in through the French windows.

Your Bourbon, Sir.

Thanks.

So, this golden bone... I guess it's worth a few bucks, huh?

It's utterly priceless!

Forged in solid gold and intricately carved by the greatest craftsmen of the ancient world...

Your milkshake, Sir.

Yum!

... It was created for Alexander the Great, as a gift to his faithful companion Ozzy ...

Who's a good boy? Who's a good doggy?

... but was almost immediately lost and remained so for many centuries.

Fetch, boy!

Go on, boy, fetch the bone!

Fetch the expensive bone!

Fetch the really, really expensive bone...

We can only guess at what happened...

Oh dear.

Its later history is hazy but bloody. So many lives were lost in its pursuit that some said the bone was cursed. By the mid seventeenth century it was lost again and many thought it no more than a myth.

My grandfather learned of the bone's existence in 1931 and immediately knew that he had to make it his own.

He commissioned the famous adventurer Idaho Smith to seek it out. Smith tracked it down to Borneo and brought it back to this country ...

... where it has remained in the Woofington family's possession ... until this morning.

I presume the bone was kept somewhere suitably secure?

Shlluurrp

Burp!

ching!

Aye. You can't be too careful.

Well normally it wouldn't be kept in the house at all.

Usually it stays in the high security vault of Barkly's Bank...

Phew!

... and this replica remains on display here.

But yesterday I had the real bone brought here secretly to show to Lady Agatha Dumfries who was paying a visit.

Coo.

Somehow the thieves knew all about it. They ignored the fake and stole the real bone from the safe...

Cardigan, take down Sir Henry, could you.

Certainly, Sir.

No sign of forced entry. And none of the alarms were triggered. They're clever devils I fear.

It's a professional job all right. Who might have done it?

Hmm...

Oh, now ... what's this?

Maybe the Bixley Twins... Or the Lamp Street Gang...

Ooh, a book of matches!

Weird how often that happens!

"The Club Fifi"

Say – isn't that place run by...?

WAH WAH JOHNSON!

That lowdown hound! He won't escape from me this time!

THWACK

Come on, McBoo.

We're going to see a dog about a bone!

Well, well... Kirk Bergman!

So good to see you again.

And this must be your new partner...?

Duncan McBoo. Pleased to meet you, Mr Johnson.

Charmed.

Hmm ... he's bigger than the last fellow isn't he?

Sturdy.

Maybe he'll last a little longer, eh?

GRRRRR!

So, what can I do for you, gentlemen? I'm always eager to help the police with their enquiries.

And let's face it, you need all the help you can get.

Can it, Johnson!

We know you've got the Golden Bone!

We found this at the scene of the crime!

Oh, how marvellously quaint.

SLAM!

Head for Muttville, McBoo. We'll pay Lenny The Grass a visit.

Okey dokey.

You think he'll know where this "FB" place is?

Probably.

And do you think that the fellow in the car behind us might know too?

Eh?

He's been following us since we left Club Fifi.

Well, well ... if it isn't Pinky Green. Sure, he's one of Wah Wah's boys. He'll know.

Righto.
I'll have a word.

CRASH!

ERT!

Hello there.

Ow!

Mr Green, my name's Detective McBoo. I wonder if you could help me?

Shove off, copper!

McBoo, what do you think you're...

Oh!

You really shouldn't be so rude, Mr Green. You might upset someone.

Now, as I was saying...

Eek!

You know, it's amazing how public-spirited people can be if they're just given the right encouragement.

Farley's Bar, over on Wag St. We can be there in fifteen minutes.

SLAM!

Of course, we'll need to go undercover.

Ooh, goody! Dressing up!

9:55 p.m.

Farley's BAR

You know, McBoo, I'm just not sure about these disguises.

Are you kidding? Our own mothers wouldn't know us!

Anyway, we were lucky to find that all-night fancy dress shop at all!

Ooh, there's Wah Wah, in the corner booth there.

And look – coming in the door now... I'll bet that's the "CC" fellow that he's meeting.

Ahem, so, Uncle Gilbert, how was your trip?

Arr! It was fine.

You were right. He's going over to Wah Wah!

And I'll bet that parcel is the Golden Bone!

Gasp! Look – it's Cardigan, Sir Garfield's butler!

So, it was an inside job!

The butler did it! Who'd have guessed.

We'd better get out of here and call for back up. This place is swarming with Wah Wah's hoodlums!

Quietly does it.

Don't do anything to draw attention to yourself.

Okay.

Uh oh!

Oh!
Oh!
Oh!

Oh dear!

I think I just lost us the deposit on the costumes.

Why look – it's your detective friends.

Excellent!

GET THEM, BOYS!

Erk!

27

Before long...

You know, McBoo, that was pretty smart.

Aye. I surprise myself sometimes.

Not that I was worried at all.

No, of course not.

A breath of fresh air, perhaps?

Don't mind if I do.

No atmosphere in this place anyway.

Not so fast, gentlemen.

Spud, Curly — if you'd be so kind?

Oh dear. And just when everything was going so well.

Hello again, Spud. I like what you've done with that eye. It really suits you.

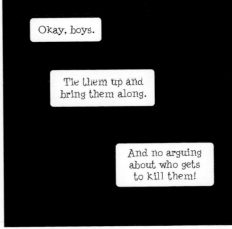

Okay, boys.

Tie them up and bring them along.

And no arguing about who gets to kill them!

sproing

SPLASH!

WAH!

SPLASH

Ach!

Aww! What did you have to do that for?

I was having such a lovely dream.

Hah! Don't you worry. You'll—

Hang on a second...

CURLY!

What do I pay you for?

Can't you see I need a box here?

That's better. Er, now where was I?

Um ... "Hah! Don't you worry. You'll—"

Ah yes. Thank you. Ahem...

Don't worry, Detective McBoo, you'll be sleeping again soon enough. You'll be sleeping **for a very long time!**

Ooh, that's no good. I need to get up early in the morning to go and visit my mum.

It's her birthday.

Gah! I didn't really mean you'd be sleeping, you idiot! I meant you'd be **dead!**

Oh. I see.

Well, that's not very nice, is it?

Nice?

It's not meant to be nice! **I'm** not meant to be nice!

I'm evil!

I'M AN EVIL GENIUS!

Oops!

WHUMP!

Nice going there, genius!

SHUT UP! SHUT UP!

At least I'm smarter than the pair of you.

Smart enough to steal the Golden Bone. And more importantly ...

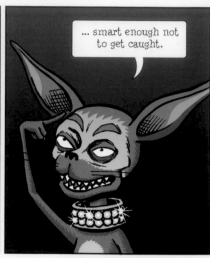

... smart enough not to get caught.

Comfortable, Mr Bergman? Ropes not too tight, I hope.

Ah, shaddup!

Ow!

Well, that hurt, Mr Bergman, but it's the last pain you will ever cause me.

Who would have thought it? All the years you've been such an irritation to me ...

... and in the end all it took to get you out of my fur ...

... all it took to lure you to your doom ...

... was a book of matches!

You set us up?

Of course, my dear boy. I **am** a genius!

Time to go, Boss.

Oh, gentlemen, I'm sorry. It's been so lovely to see you but I have a boat to catch.

A client in Cairo wishes to pay me a great deal of money for the Golden Bone and it would be rude to keep him waiting.

But I'm sure that Spud will take very good care of you for me.

Oh yes. I'll take care of you all right!

Well now, this **is** cosy, isn't it?

Alone at last.

And not a soul around for miles.

No one can save you now!

Well actually ...

... there is someone!

Oh yeah? And who's that, exactly? Your fairy godmother?

No, don't be silly.

Bartholomew Quigley will save us.

Get him, Bartholomew!

Meanwhile, just behind McBoo's ear...

What's that?

Cripes! The boss is in trouble!

To the rescue!

Stop trying to kid me, copper. There's no one...

Ooyah!

Rrrr!

Oh! Oh! Oh!

Nearly there...

Ow! Ow! Ow!

SNAP!

Ooooh ... that's better!

Okay, Bartholomew, that's enough now.

Thank you.

Ah, the relief...

Ooooh...

Oh!

WHUMP!

CRASH!

Untie me, McBoo! There's no time to lose!

Righto.

Now ...

... let's finish this thing!

Come on, McBoo. Wah Wah can't be far ahead of us.

You can't go that fast on legs as short as his.

There's Curly!

Hold it right there, Mulligan!

Boss! It's the cops!

Bergman? Curses! That dog has more lives than a cat!

Curly! Quickly!

Throw down the bone!

Okay, Boss. On three.

One, two ...

... thraaaaah!

OOF!

Nice work, McBoo.

Johnson ...

THE DOGS' DINNER

I don't know what the fuss is about. They've never done me any harm.

Oh, apart from that time I went blind...

But that was only for a couple of weeks.

Uh oh! Here come the speeches.

His worship, Mayor Flanagan.

Ladies and gentlemen...

Before we move on to the main course, I'd like to take a moment to introduce our very special chef for this evening ...

... Anton Le Boof!

Sank you, sank you.

TAR AN TARA

Yes, it is true. Tonight you are truly privileged to be served the finest dishes in all the world, prepared by moi, the great Anton Le Boof!

Cuisine Magazine's Chef of the Year!

Celebrated inventor of the chocolate sprout!

Three time winner of the Golden Crepe Award!

clap clap clap clap

clap clap clap

And highly commended for my beetroot chutney by the Neasden Women's Institute!

Yes, tonight your palates will be caressed to exquisite pleasure by the greatest delicacies ...

... prepared by the greatest genius of the culinary arts that the world has ever known!

I sank you.

Do you think there'll be jelly and ice cream for pudding? I like jelly and ice cream.

42

Evening, all!

Listen up, people!

These boys have itchy trigger fingers. Don't make them scratch!

Everybody just stay calm and still.

That means you too, Cooky!

Ulp!

Especially you, "Monsieur Le Boof!"

Sounds like they've got a beef with Le Boof, McBoo!

...McBoo?

Where are you?

I'm down here. One of my Vesuvios fell on the floor.

McBoo! Armed criminals are rampaging around the banqueting hall...

This is no time to be chasing after sweeties!

With you in a minute.

Come on, boys, this is our man.

Let's go!

Get your filthy paws off me! This is an outrage!

McBoo, you big galoot! There's police work to be done here!

Ah, there it is.

Can't wait for McBoo any longer. Guess I'll have to do this alone.

POLICE! Stop or I'll...

Hah! Or you'll what?

Throw a bread roll?

Darn you, you cheeky pup!

I'll teach you to ...

SLAM!

... keep your mouth shut!

Ulp!

Gak!

Bergman, are you okay?

RRRUUURRRGH!

NYAAAHH!

Later...

I don't need to tell you, Bergman – this looks bad for the department!

A kidnapping right under the noses of our two top dogs!

Don't sweat, Chief, we're working this case hard!

Uniform are taking statements from the guests.

And maybe the lab boys will turn up something from the bullets ...

... or the cake. If there's any left by then!

McBoo, quit eating the evidence, wouldya?!

Oop!

Um, I was just ... investigating it ...

... with my mouth.

You have to be very thorough on a case like this!

We've got our best dogs on this one, Chief. We'll soon turn something up.

That's all very well, Bergman, but what leads do you have right now?

I need fast results on this one or the press will have a field day!

The press! Of course! Now where is ...

snap

... SCOOP BAILEY!

Hold it right there, paperboy!

tippy toe

You got pictures of the whole shebang-bang, didn't you? Hand over the cameras, Scoop!

Aw, geez Louise, Bergman! I coulda won the Puppitzer Prize with those shots!

Aw, I'm weeping for you, Bailey. Those pictures are evidence now!

You'll have to console yourself with the warm glow of having done your duty as a citizen.

Sure, sure...

My editor pays me a bonus when I glow warmly.

You'll be okay, Scoop. Play nice and maybe we'll throw you a bone when we wrap this case up.

Meantime, remind me: what's the name of that restaurant critic at The Post?

Later, at the Rover Café...

Daniel Spaniel?

Yes, dear boy ... mmm ... what can I do for you?

Detective Bergman, CPD. This is my colleague, Detective McBoo.

Hullo there.

Scoop Bailey told us we might find you here...

Detectives? How thrilling! Will you join me? I seem to have rather over-ordered again.

No thanks, we already ate and we're on duty.

Um, yes. That's right.

Oh, well ... munch ... that is a shame. But tell me ... mmm yum ... how can I help you?

A jumped up burger-flipper, name of Le Boof got himself kidnapped tonight. You know him?

Oh, how ... nyum ... dreadful! Poor Anton!

But I'm afraid I won't be much help to you. I can vouch for the quality of his marrowbone soufflé but I've only actually met Anton once or twice, and then only very briefly.

Uh huh. But still, perhaps with your connections in the restaurant world you might have an idea of any enemies Le Boof might have...

Enemies?

No, no ... munch ... I've no idea. I'm afraid that the talented Monsieur Le Boof is something of ... gulp ... a mystery.

He arrived as if from nowhere a year ago and took the city by storm with his daring new recipes.

POSH NOSH! Snooty Chef Sensation!

He had a meteoric rise to the top of his profession, rave reviews from all the critics, myself among them ...

... but no scandal, no gossip, no enemies. Perhaps someone from his past but, as I say, his past is a mystery!

I see.

So sorry I can't be more help.

Detective Bergman, sir!

The lab sent me over with these for you. Said you wanted to see them as soon as possible.

Aha! Scoops's photos. Thanks, Officer Dooley.

No need to worry yourself, Spaniel. As you can see, we have other leads to work on.

Come on, McBoo.

Oh, righto. Bye bye, Mr Spaniel. Lovely to meet you.

A pleasure, dear boy.

CRASH!

SMASH!

ERK!

Oop!

Sorry about that.

Come on, McBoo!

I shall have someone attend to the mess at once, Monsieur Spaniel.

Thank you, Marcel.

And could I have another bottle of the St Radegund '24, please.

And the telephone. There's a rather important call I need to make.

Aw, come on, Frank. Jusht one more liddle drinkeroonie.

One lasht one for the road? Whaddyasay?

I say you should go home and sleep it off, Barney. You've had enough.

I'll say when I've had enough, you lousy...

WAAAH!

Excuse me, Sir, I'll be needing your stool for important police business.

You just hang around here until you've calmed down a bit.

Milkshake, please, Frank.

You stay out of trouble, McBoo. I'll find—

Why, Kirk Bergman! Second time in seven years you've come here. People will talk!

... Fifi.

You here to buy me that drink, Detective?

Or am I just helping you with your enquiries?

Quick, McBoo!

I'M GOING TO KILL YOU!

WAAAAH!

THUNK!

Sorry about that.

I didn't scare you, did I?

I've got a bit of a cockroach problem. I've been after that little monster all week!

Ouch!

Good shot though!

So, anyway, how can I help you, Detectives?

You know a dog name of Jimmy Kibble?

Sure. Jimmy worked here for a while.

He in trouble?

Not with us. But, yeah, he's in trouble. You want to help him?

Help you, you mean?

Well, yes. That too, I suppose.

Aw, go on. We'd be very grateful.

Yeah, that's right.

Maybe even grateful enough not to tell the health department about the state of your kitchen and get you closed down!

No need for that. I'm always happy to help you police dogs.

Let me just check on the customers out front and then I'll answer all your questions.

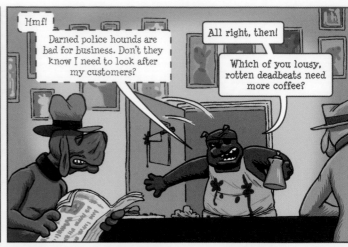

Hmf! Darned police hounds are bad for business. Don't they know I need to look after my customers?

All right, then! Which of you lousy, rotten deadbeats need more coffee?

You know, I was only joking but we really **ought** to report him. This place is **disgusting**!

When do you think he last even bothered to do any washing up?

Three or four days at least, I reckon.

Lucky for me!

Yum ... cake mix!

Mmm ... lemony!

!

Bergman! Hopper made the big cake!

What?

You're sure?

Aye! I don't know much but I do know about cake!

Right! Let's arrest Hopper and get him down to the station. We'll see what we can get out of him there.

Finally, we're—

BANG!

Aaargh!

Dammit!

Tch. As if the service in this place wasn't bad enough already!

Oh, that really is quite inconvenient!

Hopper, quickly, you may not have much time! Who did this to you?

And how did you make the sponge in the cake so light?

Nnnff.

Mmmf?

What's...?

Who's...?

A car?

What time...?

Who on earth...?

Oh, no!

Oh, dear!

Oh, no!

Hurry up!

Answer, for heaven's sake!

Oh, thank goodness!

They're here!

Yes, the detectives I told you about.

Very well. But please, hurry!

CRASH!

Knock, knock!

Hello again, Mr Spaniel.

Um, sorry about the door, Mr Spaniel. I don't know my own strength sometimes!

That's better. Now spill it, Spaniel!

All right ... glub ... all right!

I knew Kibble, it's true.

I haven't always been a reviewer of fancy restaurants. I had to work my way up from ... humbler establishments.

As such, I mixed for a while with some very shady characters.

I was delighted when my work began to take me to more respectable places and I was able to leave these underworld connections behind.

Or so I thought...

'Ullo, Spaniel, got a proposition for you.

You'll like it ...

... if you know what's good for you.

This dangerous fellow wanted to find Kibble.

I didn't ask why. I didn't wish to know.

As chance would have it, shortly afterwards I visited a new restaurant with a remarkable new chef called...

Anton Le Boof!

Yes. He pretended not to know me. As if the beard and the terrible accent would be enough to fool me.

And you told your gangster pal that Kibble was now Le Boof.

And he sent a cake full of hoods to the Mayor's dinner to snatch him.

So who is he, this gangster?

It's...

Pug Ugly!

Pug Ugly?

Excellent! I've been trying to pin something on him for years.

Come on, McBoo. Let's pay that ugly thug a visit!

Good idea...

We'll give you a lift!

Erk!

Oh, boys ...

... I promise you, you're going to regret this!

Are we nearly there yet?

Are we nearly there yet?

I did warn you.

Are we nearly there yet?

Are we nearly there yet?

WESLEY & SONS SCRAP MERCHANTS

Paws where we can see them, coppers!

So, Pug Ugly – we should have thought to look for you in a junkyard...

You must feel right at home amongst all the rubbish!

'Ullo? Who's this lippy geezer, then?

THE BONE

These are the coppers that Spaniel tipped us off about, Boss. The ones looking for Jimmy Kibble.

Hullo there, Mr Ugly. Pleased to meet you.

Looking for Jimmy, eh? Well we can 'elp you out there, as it 'appens.

JIMMY!

IN 'ERE!

NOW!

'Ere 'e is. Safe and sound.

You're a popular boy, Jimmy. These detectives are concerned for your well-being. Ain't that sweet?

Oh, well, that's lovely, Mr Ugly.

If you could just remove his leg irons we'll take Mr Kibble home and say no more about it.

Erk!

Or possibly you'd prefer it if he stayed here?

Chik

Yur.

We went to quite a bit of trouble to find 'im again so I'd like to 'ang on to 'im, ta.

See, I tried to 'ire 'im as my personal chef back when 'e was working for 'Arry 'Opper but 'e turned me down flat and did a bunk.

Bit rude, that. Didn't like it.

Didn't like it at all.

Made me irked.

Awright, Jimmy, back to work now, son.

Luckily, I've got a lot of contacts one way and another.

Fingers in a lot of pies: bars, theatres, restaurants, newspapers...

I can find out most things if I set my mind to it.

So we found Jimmy.

And we asked 'im again.

And managed to persuade 'im.

I generally do get my way.

So now Jimmy works for me and everybody's 'appy.

Oh yes. So very happy.

So you didn't kidnap Jimmy for a ransom? You went to all this trouble just so you had someone to cook your breakfast?

Most important meal of the day! And let me tell you – nobody ...

... NOBODY ...

... makes beans on toast like this boy!

Aah! Luvverly!

Beans on toast? Mmm ... yum!

Now if you just bear with me, gents ... SNURF! ... then just as soon as I'm done ... SLURP!

URP! ... we can get on with the business at hand.

I do so hate killing nosy coppers on an empty stomach!

See – that's the beauty of owning a scrapyard: it's so convenient for disposing of unwanted rubbish.

Right then, boys, bung them in that old jalopy ... ... so I can lift them with the magnet ...

... and drop them in the crusher! Lovely!

CRUSHOMATIC 3000

Any thoughts, McBoo? I wish we'd had breakfast!

Actually, I'm kinda glad you haven't been eating beans, personally...

Well, McBoo, I guess this is the end of the line.

Aye.

It's a shame, too. I always wanted to drive one of these.

Lovely wee car, the Spurling Roadmaster.

CRUS 3

Shame this one was so badly looked after though. The state of this floor...

All rusted and rotten...

Ng!

STOMP!

CRUNCH!

Oh!

Aha!

If we can both...

Keep stomping, McBoo! Stomp for your life!

STOMP! STOMP!

Nyah!

STOMP! STOMP!

Nnf!

Let's see, now...

A little bit to the left ...

SMASH!

... and 'ere we go.

MAGNET OFF ON

Okay, McBoo — time for police procedure 23B.

Oh, aye? What's that then?

RUN!

PLAP!

Ooh, look, it's raining firearms!

McBoo! Watch out!

Oop!

WAAAAAAAAHH!

Ooooooh!

Ah!

Aarghh!

Oof!

Ow!

Wah!

CRASH!

Hup!

Phew!

Now where's...?

Everything under control here, McBoo?

Aye. But what about Ugly? Did he get away?

Oh no, he's still hanging around!

'Elp!

Get me down!

Later, at police HQ...

Masterful work, Detectives! Quite superb! You're a credit to the force.

Okay, Chief, calm down!

That's right, Chief. Don't make a meal of it!

THE END